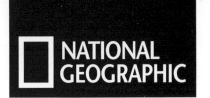

Windows on Literacy

ASSESSMENT HANDBOOK · FLUENT STAGE · SET A

Published by the National Geographic Society, Washington, D.C. 20036.

Windows on Literacy program developed by Barrie Publishing Pty Limited and Gilt Edge Publishing.

ISBN: 0-7922-8759-2

Product #41128

Produced through the worldwide resources of the National Geographic Society, John M. Fahey, Jr., President and Chief Executive Officer; Gilbert M. Grosvenor, Chairman of the Board; Nina D. Hoffman, Executive Vice President and President, Books and School Publishing.

PREPARED BY NATIONAL GEOGRAPHIC
SCHOOL PUBLISHING
Ericka Markman, Senior Vice President; Steve Mico, Editorial Director; Marianne Hiland, Editorial Manager; Lori Dibble Collins, Project Editor; Jim Hiscott, Design Manager; Matt Wascavage, Manager of Publishing Services; Sean Philpotts, Production Coordinator.

Production: Clifton M. Brown III, Manufacturing and Quality Control.

Design: Steven Curtis Design, Inc.

Contents

Assessment Overview 4

Observational Checklists 6

Retellings 8

Graphic Organizers 11

Oral Reading Records 17

Fluent Titles 52

Assessment Overview

Although one purpose of assessment is to measure performance so that results can be shared with parents and school administrators, its primary purpose is to gather information to inform instruction. Assessment offers valuable insights into children's learning and allows teachers to plan instruction that supports and challenges children based on their individual needs. It deals with both the knowledge children attain as well as the process of learning.

- An assessment program needs to be **ongoing** so that changes over time in children's learning can be noted and appropriate adjustments to an instructional program can be made in a timely fashion.

- An assessment program also needs to be **multidimensional** as no one assessment tool can measure the many dimensions of the complex process of learning to read.

- An assessment program needs to include both **formal** and **informal** tools so that evaluation of performance is reliable and useful.

Assessment Tools

Observational Checklists

The observational checklist on page 7 is useful for recording specific reading behaviors that describe developmental growth in young readers. Checklists can be used throughout the year to note changes in attitudes, skills, and processing strategies. They can be used to

- talk with parents about broad changes in a child's approach to reading;

- guide a teacher's observations of children using the reading process and the various cueing systems;

- provide a framework for making the same observations from child to child.

Observational Checklist

Retellings

Retellings offer a means to evaluate the quality of a child's comprehension of a text. Retellings provide insight into what the reader thought were the important parts as well as what reactions the reader had to the text. Retellings of nonfiction help teachers assess whether children understood the main ideas and recognized those details that support the main ideas. Although retellings do not represent a reader's complete understanding, they do provide a tool that gives insight into how the child processed the information in the text.

Graphic Organizers

Nonfiction texts use a variety of organization patterns to present information. Graphic organizers are excellent tools to help children reconstruct the information they learned from the books. Because graphic organizers help to represent information visually, they can be used to assess children's understanding of informational text as well as their ability to communicate their understanding in different ways.

Oral Reading Records

Using an Oral Reading Record, also known as a Running Record, allows a teacher to assess a child's accuracy in word recognition. As the child reads, the teacher uses a coding system to record each word that is read accurately as well as errors, self-corrections, and the probable strategies and cueing systems used to figure out challenging words. The notations made during the oral reading can help teachers diagnose the kinds of challenges the child is experiencing and plan instruction to match that child's needs at that time.

Oral Reading Record

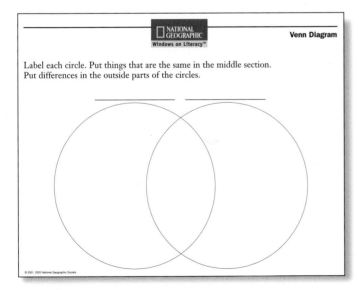

Venn Diagram

Observational Checklists

Observational checklists are tools for gathering ongoing data about an individual's reading attitudes, behaviors, and strategies. Although teachers may use a variety of tools for recording observations—anecdotal records, reading conference notes—the observational checklist can provide structure to these observations. It can provide a frame of reference for the anecdotal information that you collect.

Observational checklists are often tied to curriculum goals and help teachers focus on the behaviors and strategies that reflect the central goals of the curriculum. They work as a framework that helps teachers make the same observations from child to child. They are useful in planning instruction as well as discussing goals with individual children. Observational checklists show progress across time and help parents understand the broad changes in their child's reading.

Using Observational Checklists

Using Observational Checklists

Use the observational checklist on page 7 to assess some of the developmental behaviors and strategies that readers use during reading. These include

- attitudes about reading and books;
- understandings of books and print conventions;
- strategies used to monitor one's understanding;
- strategies used to self-correct;
- strategies used to access the various cueing systems that support readers.

You may wish to use this checklist throughout the year or you may wish to modify or add to it as your goals change.

Observational checklists are most effective when they reflect the central goals of the reading curriculum. You may find it useful to meet with other teachers and reading specialists in your school to review the observational checklist provided on page 7 and modify it to match the specific goals of your reading program.

This checklist provides a comment column to record anecdotal information that supports and explains the child's attention to a specific strategy or behavior. Anecdotal records are the important observations made of a child's work that have implications for planning future instruction. These notes can add a new level of understanding that can not be captured on tests or work samples.

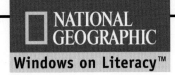

Name _____ Date _____

Grade _____ Age _____

Strategies and Behaviors	often	sometimes	never	Comments
Enjoys participating in book discussions				
Chooses to read independently				
Reads across a range of genres and forms				
Uses text features to preview books, find information, and understand how information is organized				
Gathers information from a variety of visual sources, including pictures, graphs, charts and diagrams				
Uses writing for a variety of purposes				
Summarizes and retells information				
Acquires and uses new vocabulary				
Uses multiple strategies to figure out unknown words				
Uses prior knowledge to construct meaning				
Uses questioning to clarify meaning and to find information				
Recognizes when meaning breaks down				
Uses a variety of strategies to self-correct				
Recognizes that authors use different organization patterns to present information				

Retellings

R etellings are a valuable tool for assessing a child's comprehension of an informational piece. Retellings provide insight into the child's memory, response, and understanding of the text. Retellings allow teachers to tap into the child's process of constructing meaning from the text. They reveal what information the child took away from the text, how important that information seems to the child, and how the child integrates that information with prior knowledge.

Unaided and Aided Retellings

An unaided retelling is done by asking the child to tell you everything he remembers about the book. Tell the child to assume that you have not read the book and he is to tell you everything about it. During the unaided retelling, be careful not to interrupt or provide assistance. Be friendly and encouraging, but avoid evaluative responses. If you suspect that the child knows more than he is telling, consider shifting to an aided retelling by asking questions that prompt additional information.

An aided retelling is done by asking questions that you have prepared in advance. These may prompt the child to tell about the most important ideas, how the child reacted to the book, and whether the child can relate the book to any experience in his life. The questions shown on page 9 serve as a model for planning an aided retelling.

Evaluating Retellings

You may wish to use a checklist or a rubric to help you evaluate retellings. The checklist provided on page 10 can be used with most nonfiction titles to help measure the child's understanding and his use of text supports and reading strategies. The rubric that follows is a general rubric that can be used with all nonfiction texts.

Retelling Rubric

4	The child fully explains the main ideas of the book and provides supporting details for those main ideas.
3	The child adequately explains the main ideas of the book and provides some supporting details for the main ideas.
2	The child explains most of the main ideas of the book but is not able to supply many supporting details. The retelling may contain some inaccuracies and contain very little information.
1	The child is not able to identify the main ideas or supporting details. Information is minimal and often inaccurate.

Using Retellings with *Windows on Literacy*

The following books in the Fluent collection are especially suited for retellings.

Level 13
Looking for a New House
This Is My Street

Level 14
Can You See an Insect?

Level 15
Corn
When a Storm Comes
Where Does the Water Go?

Level 16
Mapping North America

Level 17
Desert Rain
Magnets
Peanuts
Soil
The Key to Maps

Level 18
River Life
Tunnels

Name _____   Date _____

Book Title _____   Age _____

Use these questions to prompt children. Record their answers.

1. What is this book about?
2. What is the most important information in the book?
3. Did you like the book? Why or why not?
4. What was the most interesting part of the book?
5. What did you learn from this book?
6. What else would you like to learn about this topic?
7. Use the other side of the paper to have the child draw a picture of the information in this book.

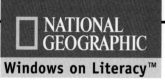

NATIONAL GEOGRAPHIC

Windows on Literacy™

Retelling Checklist

Name _____ Date _____

Book Title _____ Age _____

The retelling was   aided _____

                     unaided _____

Main Ideas

All the main ideas were included   _____

Most of the main ideas were included   _____

Some of the main ideas were included   _____

Supporting Details

Supporting details were included and logically related
to the main ideas   _____

Supporting details were included but not related
to the main ideas   _____

Few supporting details were included   _____

Use of Text Supports and Reading Strategies

Reader used photographs and illustrations
to understand text   _____

Reader made valid inferences   _____

Reader drew logical conclusions   _____

Reader asked important questions   _____

Additional Observations

Graphic Organizers

Graphic organizers help to represent information visually. They can be used to assess children's understanding of informational text as well as their ability to communicate it in different ways. Graphic organizers are excellent tools to help children reconstruct the information they learned from the books.

The books in *Windows on Literacy* offer an opportunity for children to present information in a variety of ways. In using graphic organizers with beginning readers

- show the child the diagram or chart;
- explain its purpose;
- have the child use the book to complete the diagram or chart.

Kinds of Organizers

Venn Diagram (page 13)

Explain that this chart, called a Venn diagram, can be used to show how two things are alike and different. Label each circle. Record 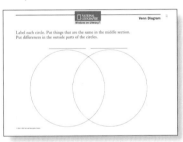 similarities in the overlapping section of the two circles. Record differences in the other parts of the circles. Use a Venn diagram with these titles:

- *Our Town*
- *This Is My Street*

Classification Chart (page 14)

Explain that this chart can be used to show how things can be sorted into groups. Record the category at the top of each column.  Then put specific examples in the appropriate columns. Use a classification chart with these titles:

- *Going Up the Mountain*
- *The Rain Forest*
- *Using Rocks*

Flowchart (page 15)

Explain that this chart, called a flowchart, can be used to show the steps to make something. Record the first step in the

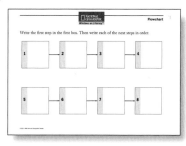

first box and then record the subsequent steps in order. Use a flowchart with these titles:

- *From Field to Florist*
- *Ice Cream for You*
  (Note: Use with Chapter 2 to show the seven steps in Making Ice Cream. One box will be blank.)
- *My Fish Tank*
- *The Car Wash*
  (Note: Two boxes will be blank.)
- *Turn on the Faucet*
  (Note: One box will be blank.)
- *Water Can Change*
  (Note: Use the top row to show the three steps in Ice and the bottom row to show the three steps in Water.)

Concept Web (page 16)

Explain that this chart, called a concept web, can be used to show the main idea and supporting details. Record the main

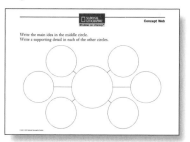

idea in the middle circle. Record the supporting details in the surrounding circles. Use a concept web with these titles:

- *A Cat's Whiskers*
- *Holidays*
- *Machines Make Fun Rides*
  (Note: Three circles will be blank.)
- *Mighty Machines*
- *More Places to Visit*
- *Spiders Spin Silk*
  (Note: One circle will be blank.)
- *Wind Power*

Label each circle. Put things that are the same in the middle section.
Put differences in the outside parts of the circles.

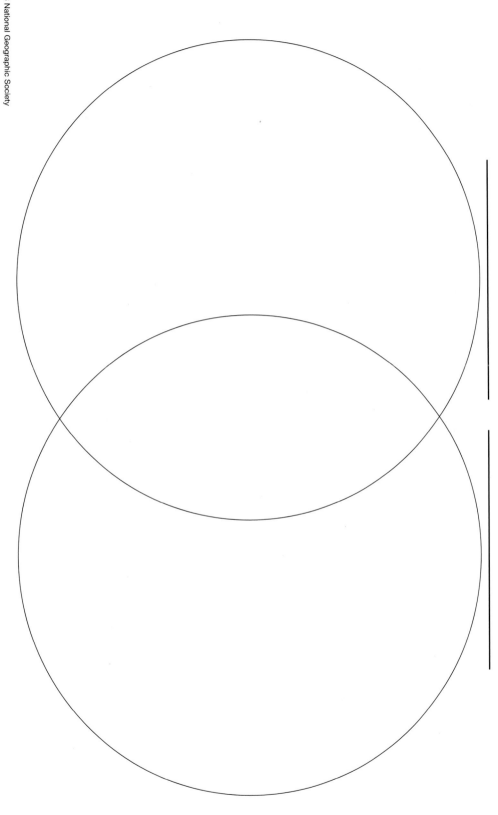

Label each column. Write examples in each column.

Write the first step in the first box. Then write each of the next steps in order.

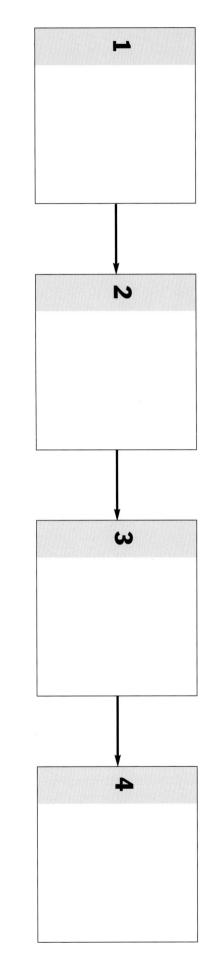

| 1 |
| 2 |
| 3 |
| 4 |

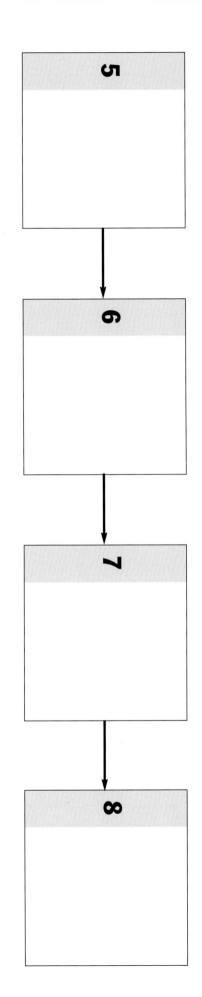

| 5 |
| 6 |
| 7 |
| 8 |

Write the main idea in the middle circle.
Write a supporting detail in each of the other circles.

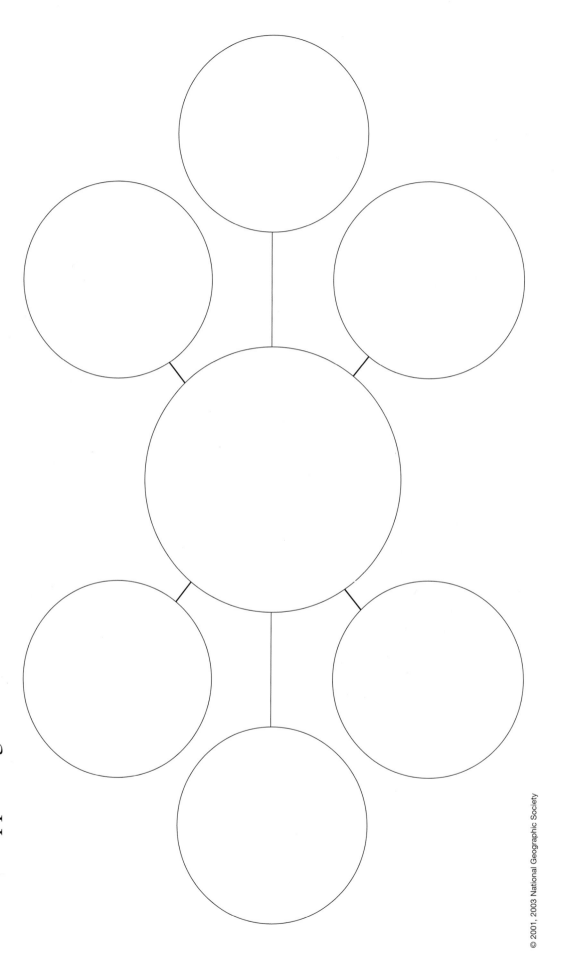

Oral Reading Records

Oral reading records, also called running records, are powerful tools that provide a framework for teachers to systematically observe and interpret a child's reading behaviors. They give insight into how a child is using reading strategies and cueing systems.

Although taking oral reading records does require some practice, once teachers become comfortable with the technique, most find these to be relatively easy to do. More importantly, they provide information that helps to monitor individual growth and to plan instruction.

Taking Oral Reading Records

1. Establish a Rotating Schedule

Plan to take oral reading records for each child frequently so that you can monitor progress and adjust instruction as needed. A goal might be to record each child's reading every few weeks. Set up a rotating schedule so that you spend some time each day taking oral reading records.

2. Learn the Coding System

Oral reading records use a standard set of conventions to record a child's reading behaviors as she reads. You need to become comfortable with these to feel confident in taking oral reading records. These include

- Using a check mark (✓) for each word read correctly.

- For each miscue, draw a horizontal line above the miscue. Write the reader's behavior above the line. If the child self-corrects the miscue, add *sc* to show the self-correction. For example, for a child who reads *dog* for *puppy*, and then self corrects, you would write

$$\text{✓ ✓ ✓ } \frac{sc}{dog}$$
We buy a puppy.

- If the child omits a word, draw a line through the omitted word.

- If the child inserts a word, insert a ^ and write the inserted word above the text.

- If the child substitutes a word, draw a line through the original word and write the substituted word above it.

[For a thorough discussion of these conventions, see Clay, M. M. (1993) *An Observation Survey of Early Literacy Achievement*, Portsmouth, NH, Heinenman.]

3. Select the Text

You can use a book that the child has already read to evaluate how well the child is using strategies that have been taught. You can use a new to evaluate the child's use of cueing systems. The text needs to provide enough challenges so that the child makes some miscues; otherwise no information is gathered from the experience.

4. Observe the Child Reading

Use the oral reading records provided in this book to record observations. For each level, the text of two titles are printed on forms. Use the blank form provided on page 20 to use other books from *Windows on Literacy*. Sit beside or behind the child so that you can observe the reading. Avoid teaching, but you can provide a word when asked or suggest that the child try it again if you think a reread of some text would be helpful.

5. Have the Child Retell

After the reading, ask the child to retell everything she can remember about the text. Record your impressions of the retelling. See Retellings on page 8.

6. Analyze the Oral Reading Record

An analysis of the record helps you determine the difficulty level of the text for that child and also provides insight into the child's use of strategies and cueing systems.

Understanding a child's use of strategies and cueing systems requires a careful analysis of each error and each self-correction. You will be judging whether the child is using one or more of these cueing systems.

- **Meaning** Meaning, or semantic, cues are those based on the context of the text. A child who substitutes *puppy* for *dog* is using the meaning of the story to predict text.

- **Structure** Structure, or syntactic, cues are those based on grammar, syntax, and language structure. A child who substitutes *went* for *wanted* knows that a past tense verb is correct but is not using meaning to confirm the correct verb.

- **Visual Information** Graphic cues are based on visual information and/or phonic cues. A child who reads *closed* for *closing* is not paying attention to word endings.

7. Using the Reading Record Summary

The form on page 19 allows you to compile information and analyze the results of the Oral Reading Record. This form allows you to note general print awareness and strategies used when encountering unknown words and when making an error.

The second section of the form will help you to determine the child's reading level, which is important in choosing books for individuals.

- To determine the error rate, divide the total number of words read by the total number of errors made. This will give you a ratio. For example, a child who read a total of 60 words and made 4 errors, has an error rate of 1:15. The child made one error for every 15 words read.

- The accuracy rate is the percentage of words read correctly. So a child reading 56 words correctly out of a total of 60 words is reading at a 93% accuracy rate. This helps to determine the level of reading.

  - 95%–100% is an independent or easy reading level

  - 90%–94% is an instructional level

  - below 90% is a difficult or frustration level

- Self-corrections are positive reading behaviors. To determine a child's self-correction rate, add the number of errors and the number of self-corrections. Then divide this total by the number of self-corrections. This will give you a ratio. For example, a child who has a self-correction rate of 1:3 is able to recognize an error and correct it one out of every three times. A self-correction rate of 1:3 to 1:5 is considered good.

The form also allows you to add notes on the child's retelling and make notes on your overall analysis of reading behaviors.

8. Use the Results

Oral Reading Records yield a wealth of information about individual readers. Use the results from the accuracy and error rate score to determine if a text is too difficult for a child. Use the analysis of errors and self-corrections to plan instruction for individuals or groups. This analysis is also useful in talking with parents and other teachers.

Name: _____ Age: _____ Date: _____

Text: _____ Level: _____ Seen/Unseen

Strategies Used

Directionality   1 to 1 Matching   Phrased Reading (using punctuation)   Fluent Reading

At an Unknown Word

Makes No Attempt   Attempts by Using:

Seeks Help   ____ Letter/Sound Knowledge

Reruns   ____ Meaning

Reads On   ____ Syntax

After an Error

Ignores   Self-corrects Using:

Seeks Help   ____ Letter/Sound Knowledge

Reruns   ____ Meaning

Attempts SC   ____ Syntax

Reading Level

Error Rate $\dfrac{\text{No. of Words}}{\text{No. of Errors}}$ = 1:   _____ Easy/Independent

Accuracy %   _____ Instructional

S/C Rate $\dfrac{(ER + SC)}{SC}$ = 1:   _____ Difficult/Frustration

Notes on Oral Retelling

Analysis of Reading Behaviors

Recommendations:

Teacher: _____   Date: _____

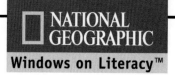

Oral Reading Record

Name: _____ Age: _____ Date: _____

Book Title: _____ Level: _____ Words: _____

Accuracy: _____ S.C. Rate: _____

PAGE	TEXT	ER	SC	ER MSV	SC MSV
	TOTAL				

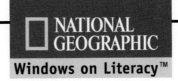

Oral Reading Record

Name: _____   Age: _____   Date: _____

Book Title: **Big Red Tomatoes**   Level: **13**   Words: **168**

Accuracy: _____   S.C. Rate: _____

PAGE	TEXT	ER	SC	ER MSV	SC MSV
2	Big red tomatoes are smooth				
	and round and juicy.				
4	They taste good				
	in a salad.				
	They taste good				
	in a sandwich.				
5	They taste good in a sauce.				
6	Where do tomatoes come from?				
	They are grown on farms.				
7	They are grown from seeds.				
8	Farmers put the tomato seeds into pots of soil.				
9	Soon, the seeds sprout.				
	Tiny leaves push up through the soil.				
10	The little tomato plants are called seedlings.				
	SUBTOTAL				

PAGE	TEXT	ER	SC	ER MSV	SC MSV
11	The seedlings grow into plants.				
	Farmers plant the tomato plants in long rows				
	on their farms.				
12	Water and sunshine				
	help the plants grow.				
	Little yellow flowers start to grow				
	among the leaves.				
14	A tiny tomato forms				
	in the middle of the flower.				
15	At first the tomato is green.				
16	It grows bigger				
	and bigger.				
	Then, as it ripens,				
	it turns red.				
18	People pick the tomatoes.				
	SUBTOTAL				

Name: _____   Book Title: __**Big Red Tomatoes (Cont.)**__

PAGE	TEXT	ER	SC	ER MSV	SC MSV
20	The tomatoes are packed				
	into boxes.				
	Then they are sent				
	to markets.				
21	People buy big red tomatoes.				
22	They mix them				
	in a salad.				
	They eat them				
	in a sandwich.				
23	They cook them				
	in a sauce.				
	TOTAL				

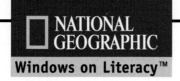

Oral Reading Record

Name: _____   Age: _____   Date: _____

Book Title: _____ **Our Town** _____   Level: ___ **13** ___   Words: ___ **129** ___

Accuracy: _____   S.C. Rate: _____

PAGE	TEXT	ER	SC	ER MSV	SC MSV
2	Our town used to be very small.				
3	Now it is much bigger.				
	Many people moved to the town.				
	The town has grown and changed.				
4	There used to be lots of open space around our town.				
5	Now there are lots of houses.				
	People built more houses as the town grew.				
6	There used to be dirt roads in our town.				
7	Now there are paved roads.				
	People built the paved roads as the town grew.				
8	There used to be only a few stores in our town.				
9	Now there are many stores.				
	People built more stores as the town grew.				
	SUBTOTAL				

PAGE	TEXT	ER	SC	ER MSV	SC MSV
10	There used to be one small school in our town.				
11	Now there are many large schools.				
	People built more schools as the town grew.				
12	Do you know how your town used to look?				
	TOTAL				

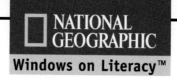

Oral Reading Record

Name: _____   Age: _____   Date: _____

Book Title: __**From Field to Florist**__   Level: __14__   Words: __142__

Accuracy: _____   S.C. Rate: _____

PAGE	TEXT	ER	SC	ER MSV	SC MSV
2	Look at all the flowers.				
	They are for sale in a flower store.				
3	A person who sells flowers is called a florist.				
	Where does the florist get all the flowers?				
4	Farmers grow the flowers.				
	Some of the flowers are grown in large fields.				
5	Some of the flowers are grown in greenhouses.				
6	In the morning, farmers cut the flowers				
	they will sell at the market.				
	They put the cut flowers				
	in their truck.				
7	They take their flowers to the market.				
8	At the market the flowers are kept				
	in buckets full of water.				
	The water helps keep the flowers fresh.				
	SUBTOTAL				

Name: _____   Book Title: __**From Field to Florist (Cont.)**__

PAGE	TEXT	ER	SC	ER MSV	SC MSV
9	Florists visit the market.				
	This is where they get the flowers				
	to sell in their stores.				
10	The florist gets the flowers ready to sell at the store.				
	Some of the flowers are made up into bunches.				
12	People buy flowers at the flower store.				
	TOTAL				

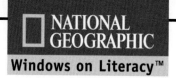

Oral Reading Record

Name: _____   Age: _____   Date: _____

Book Title: **How Does My Bike Work?**   Level: **14**   Words: **127**

Accuracy: _____   S.C. Rate: _____

PAGE	TEXT	ER	SC	ER MSV	SC MSV
2	I am riding my bike.				
	Look at how my bike works.				
3	I push down on one pedal.				
	I push down on the other pedal.				
	I make the pedals go around.				
4	When I make the pedals go around,				
	they turn a big sprocket.				
5	When the big sprocket goes around,				
	it turns the chain.				
6	When the chain goes around,				
	it turns a small sprocket.				
7	When the small sprocket goes around,				
	it turns the back wheel.				
	When the back wheel goes around,				
	my bike moves forward.				
	SUBTOTAL				

Name: _____ Book Title: **How Does My Bike Work? (Cont.)**

PAGE	TEXT	ER	SC	ER MSV	SC MSV
8	When I need to turn,				
	I turn the handlebars.				
9	When I turn the handlebars,				
	the front wheel turns.				
	My bike turns.				
10	When I squeeze the brake lever,				
	the brake pads press against the tires.				
	My bike slows down.				
11	This is how my bike works.				
	TOTAL				

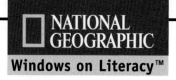

Oral Reading Record

Name: _____   Age: _____   Date: _____

Book Title: _____**Jack's Boat**_____   Level: ____**15**____   Words: ____**172**____

Accuracy: _____   S.C. Rate: _____

PAGE	TEXT	ER	SC	ER MSV	SC MSV
2	Jack is a fisherman.				
	He has a big fishing boat.				
	Every day Jack goes out to sea.				
	He takes his boat out to sea				
	to catch fish.				
4	People work on Jack's fishing boat.				
	They are called the crew.				
	The crew help Jack catch fish.				
5	The crew throw the fishing nets				
	into the water.				
6	The crew drag in the nets.				
	Then they sort the fish.				
8	At the end of the trip,				
	Jack takes the boat back to the dock.				
	SUBTOTAL				

© 2001, 2003 National Geographic Society

PAGE	TEXT	ER	SC	ER MSV	SC MSV
9	The crew unload the boat.				
	They load the fish onto a truck.				
	The fish are ready to be sold.				
10	The fish are taken to the market.				
	The buyer at the market				
	checks the fish.				
12	When Jack sells his fish,				
	he gets money.				
13	Jack uses some of the money				
	to pay the crew.				
14	Jack uses some of the money				
	to buy things he needs.				
15	Jack uses some of the money				
	to buy things for his boat.				
16	One day Jack will use his money				
	to buy a bigger boat.				
	Then he can catch even more fish!				
	TOTAL				

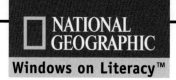

Oral Reading Record

Name: _____ Age: _____ Date: _____

Book Title: __**Sea and Land Animals**__ Level: __**15**__ Words: __**310**__

Accuracy: _____ S.C. Rate: _____

PAGE	TEXT	ER	SC	ER MSV	SC MSV
2	Animals that live in the sea may seem				
	very different from animals that live on the land.				
3	But they are not always so different.				
4	Some animals have sharp teeth to bite their food.				
	A shark has sharp teeth.				
	It uses its sharp teeth to bite into its food.				
	A shark lives in the sea.				
5	A lion has sharp teeth.				
	It uses its sharp teeth to bite into its food.				
	A lion lives on the land.				
6	Some animals have claws to tear their food.				
	A lobster has claws.				
	It uses its claws to tear its food.				
	A lobster lives in the sea.				
	SUBTOTAL				

PAGE	TEXT	ER	SC	ER MSV	SC MSV
7	A bear has claws.				
	It uses its claws to tear its food.				
	A bear lives on the land.				
8	Some animals have fur to keep them warm.				
	A sea otter has fur.				
	Its fur helps keep it warm in cold water.				
	A sea otter lives in the sea.				
9	A rabbit has fur.				
	Its fur helps keep it warm in cold weather.				
	A rabbit lives on the land.				
10	Some animals have hard shells to protect their bodies.				
	A crab has a hard shell.				
	Its hard shell protects its soft body.				
	A crab lives in the sea.				
11	A tortoise has a hard shell.				
	Its hard shell protects its soft body.				
	A tortoise lives on the land.				
	SUBTOTAL				

Name: _____ Book Title: **Sea and Land Animals (Cont.)**

PAGE	TEXT	ER	SC	ER MSV	SC MSV
12	Some animals have sharp spines				
	to protect themselves from enemies.				
	A sea urchin has sharp spines.				
	Its spines help protect it from enemies.				
	A sea urchin lives in the sea.				
13	A hedgehog has sharp spines.				
	Its spines help protect it from enemies.				
	A hedgehog lives on the land.				
14	Some animals have stripes that hide them from enemies.				
	A clown fish has stripes.				
	Its stripes help it to hide from enemies.				
	A clown fish lives in the sea.				
15	A tiger has stripes.				
	Its stripes help it to hide from enemies.				
	A tiger lives on the land.				
	TOTAL				

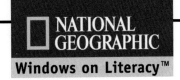

Oral Reading Record

Name: _____ Age: _____ Date: _____

Book Title: **Spiders Spin Silk** Level: **16** Words: **183**

Accuracy: _____ S.C. Rate: _____

PAGE	TEXT	ER	SC	ER MSV	SC MSV
2	Have you seen a spider web?				
	Do you know what it's made from?				
	It's made from silk.				
4	Spiders spin silk with their spinnerets.				
	The silk comes out of the spinnerets as a liquid.				
	Then it becomes a strong thread.				
	Some silk is sticky.				
6	Spiders spin silk wherever they go.				
	They spin a long line of silk behind them.				
	This line of silk is called a dragline.				
	Spiders use their draglines to escape from danger.				
8	Spiders can climb down draglines				
	to the ground.				
	They can climb up their draglines				
	to their webs.				
	SUBTOTAL				

PAGE	TEXT	ER	SC	ER MSV	SC MSV
9	Some spiders swing on their draglines to catch insects.				
10	Spiders spin silk to build homes.				
	This spider spins a silky home in a leaf.				
11	This spider spins silk to line its underground home.				
12	Spiders spin silk to build webs.				
	Spiders catch insects in their sticky webs.				
13	Some spiders wrap the insect in silk.				
	The insect cannot escape.				
14	Female spiders spin silk				
	to make a bag for their eggs.				
	The silk bag protects the spider's eggs.				
15	When baby spiders hatch, they spin silk.				
	They spin a line of silk wherever they go.				
	TOTAL				

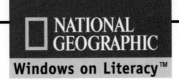
Name: _____ Age: _____ Date: _____

Book Title: _____**Work Vehicles**_____ Level: ____**16**____ Words: ____**245**____

Accuracy: _____ S.C. Rate: _____

PAGE	TEXT	ER	SC	ER MSV	SC MSV
2	How do people decide				
	what kind of vehicle to drive?				
	Many people choose a vehicle				
	that is good for their work.				
3	I am a gardener.				
	I mow lawns and take care of plants.				
	Do you know which vehicle				
	I drive at work?				
4	I need a vehicle that can carry				
	my lawn mower.				
	I need a vehicle that can carry				
	plants and tools.				
	I drive a pickup truck at work.				
	SUBTOTAL				

Name: _____   Book Title: ___**Work Vehicles (Cont.)**___

PAGE	TEXT	ER	SC	ER MSV	SC MSV
5	I am a messenger.				
	I deliver packages all over the city.				
	Do you know which vehicle				
	I drive at work?				
6	I need a vehicle that is easy to park.				
	I need a vehicle that can carry				
	small packages.				
	I drive a motorcycle at work.				
7	I am a nurse.				
	I visit patients in their homes.				
	Do you know which vehicle				
	I drive at work?				
8	I need a vehicle that can get me				
	to places quickly.				
	I need a vehicle that can carry				
	my workbag.				
	I drive a car at work.				
	SUBTOTAL				

PAGE	TEXT	ER	SC	ER MSV	SC MSV
9	I am an electrician.				
	I fix the wiring in people's homes.				
	Do you know which vehicle				
	I drive at work?				
10	I need a vehicle that has lots				
	of space.				
	I need a vehicle that can keep				
	my tools dry.				
	I drive a van at work.				
11	I am a chauffeur.				
	I take people places.				
	Do you know which vehicle				
	I drive at work?				
12	I need a vehicle that can seat				
	many people.				
	I need a vehicle that is				
	comfortable to ride in.				
	I drive a limousine at work.				
	TOTAL				

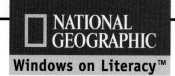

Oral Reading Record

Name: _____ Age: _____ Date: _____

Book Title: _____Fossils_____ Level: __17__ Words: __238__

Accuracy: _____ S.C. Rate: _____

PAGE	TEXT	ER	SC	ER MSV	SC MSV
2	A fossil is the remains of an animal				
	or plant that lived long ago.				
	This bone is a fossil.				
	It's the skull, or head bone, of a dinosaur				
	that lived millions of years ago.				
3	Look at this rock.				
	Can you see the leaf?				
	The leaf is a fossil, too.				
4	Fossils can be made from anything				
	that lived long ago.				
	These tree trunks are fossils.				
5	These footprints are fossils.				
6	These bones are from a dinosaur.				
	When the dinosaur died,				
	the soft parts of its body rotted away.				
	SUBTOTAL				

PAGE	TEXT	ER	SC	ER MSV	SC MSV
7	Its teeth and bones became hard				
	like stone.				
8	Most fossils are found in a special rock				
	that has built up over millions of years.				
	Finding fossils is hard, dirty work.				
	Scientists can spend months				
	looking for fossils.				
10	Scientists look at a fossil carefully.				
	A skeleton, or set of bones,				
	may be buried under it.				
11	Scientists use small shovels, picks,				
	and hammers to dig up the rocks				
	around the fossil.				
12	The fossils are sent to a museum.				
	Scientists clean the fossils.				
	They chip away the rest of the rock.				
	Then they put the bones together				
	to make a skeleton.				
	SUBTOTAL				

PAGE	TEXT	ER	SC	ER MSV	SC MSV
14	Scientists study the fossils				
	to learn more about animals				
	that lived long ago.				
	This dinosaur had sharp teeth.				
	It was a meat-eating dinosaur.				
15	This dinosaur had horns.				
	It could protect itself against enemies.				
16	People can see fossils in museums.				
	They can look at the skeletons				
	of dinosaurs.				
	Fossils help us find out about animals				
	and plants that lived long ago.				
	TOTAL				

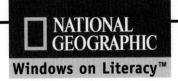

Oral Reading Record

Name: _____   Age: _____   Date: _____

Book Title: __**Places to Visit**__   Level: __17__   Words: __202__

Accuracy: _____   S.C. Rate: _____

PAGE	TEXT	ER	SC	ER MSV	SC MSV
2	There are many famous places to visit in the United States. Have you been to the Grand Canyon? It is in Arizona.				
3	The Grand Canyon is a deep valley with steep sides. In some paces it is 18 miles wide. Other places are less than one mile wide.				
4	Have you been to Yellowstone National Park?				
	SUBTOTAL				

PAGE	TEXT	ER	SC	ER MSV	SC MSV
5	It is in Wyoming, Idaho, and Montana. Yellowstone is the oldest National Park in the world. It is one of the largest safe areas for wildlife in the United States.				
6	Have you been to Niagara Falls? It is in New York.				
7	Niagara Falls is the largest waterfall in North America. It is made up of two waterfalls, the Horseshoe Falls and the American Falls.				
8	Have you been to Mount St. Helens? It is in Washington.				
	SUBTOTAL				

Name: _____   Book Title: _____ **Places to Visit (Cont.)** _____

PAGE	TEXT	ER	SC	ER MSV	SC MSV
9	Mount St. Helens is a volcano.				
	It erupted in 1980 forming a crater				
	on top.				
10	Have you been to				
	Mammoth Cave?				
	It is in Kentucky.				
11	Mammoth Cave is a				
	huge underground cave.				
	There are stalactites and				
	underground lakes in the cave.				
12	Have you been to the				
	Everglades?				
	It is in Florida.				
13	The Everglades				
	is a huge marsh.				
	It is known as				
	a river of grass.				
14	Have you been to these famous places?				
	TOTAL				

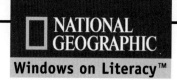

Oral Reading Record

Name: _____ Age: _____ Date: _____

Book Title: _____**Cactuses**_____ Level: __18__ Words: __237__

Accuracy: _____ S.C. Rate: _____

PAGE	TEXT	ER	SC	ER MSV	SC MSV
2	These plants all look different.				
	Some are tall. Some are short and round.				
3	All these plants are the same in some ways.				
	They are all cactuses.				
4	Most cactuses live in the desert.				
	How can cactuses grow in such a hot,				
	dry place? Cactuses have special parts				
	that help them live in the desert.				
5	Different parts of a cactus help the plant				
	collect and store water. Cactuses get bigger				
	when they soak up rainwater.				
6	Most cactuses have thick stems.				
	These stems help them live in the desert.				
	When it rains, cactuses can store a lot of				
	water in their stems.				
	SUBTOTAL				

PAGE	TEXT	ER	SC	ER MSV	SC MSV
7	Many cactuses have ribs on their stems.				
	These ribs help them live in the desert.				
	They shade the cactus from the sun				
	and help keep the plant cool.				
8	Cactuses have very long roots.				
	These long roots help them live in the desert.				
	The roots can collect a lot of water.				
9	Most cactuses have waxy skin.				
	This waxy skin helps them live in the desert.				
	The waxy skin helps keep water in the plant.				
10	Most cactuses have prickly, or sharp, spines.				
	The sharp spines help them live in the desert.				
	The sharp spines stop animals from eating				
	the cactus.				
	SUBTOTAL				

PAGE	TEXT	ER	SC	ER MSV	SC MSV
11	All cactuses produce flowers.				
	The flowers help them live in the desert.				
	The flowers form seeds so new cactuses grow.				
	Some cactus flowers bloom for less than a day!				
12	How is this cactus like other cactuses?				
	How is it different?				
	TOTAL				

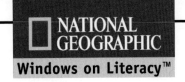
Name: _____   Age: _____   Date: _____

Book Title: __**The River's Journey**__   Level: __18__   Words: __218__

Accuracy: _____   S.C. Rate: _____

PAGE	TEXT	ER	SC	ER MSV	SC MSV
2	Have you ever seen a river?				
	A river is a large stream				
	of flowing water. This river				
	is the Mississippi River.				
	It flows through the United States.				
4	Look at this map of the United States.				
	It shows where the Mississippi River begins				
	and ends. Let's follow the Mississippi River				
	on its long journey.				
6	Where a river begins is called its source.				
	The Mississippi River begins in a lake				
	in Minnesota. It starts out as a small,				
	clear stream.				
	SUBTOTAL				

Name: _____   Book Title: __**The River's Journey (Cont.)**__

PAGE	TEXT	ER	SC	ER MSV	SC MSV
8	Other small streams flow into the Mississippi River. The river gets bigger and faster. At the Falls of St. Anthony, the river flows through locks. Locks raise or lower the water, helping boats to travel on the river.				
10	The Mississippi River flows down to lower land. It flows more slowly over the flat land. It begins to wind back and forth. The flat land around the river is called its floodplain.				
12	The river slows near the end of its journey. It drops the mud and soil that it collected further upstream. The mud and soil form new land called a delta. The Mississippi Delta is very large.				
	SUBTOTAL				

PAGE	TEXT	ER	SC	ER MSV	SC MSV
14	The end of a river is called its mouth. A river's mouth empties into another body of water. The Mississippi River empties into the Gulf of Mexico. The river's long journey has ended.				
	TOTAL				

Fluent Titles

A Cat's Whiskers

Big Red Tomatoes

Cactuses

Can You See an Insect?

Corn

Desert Rain

Fossils

From Field to Florist

Going Up the Mountain

Holidays

How Does My Bike Work?

Ice Cream for You

Jack's Boat

Looking for a New House

Machines Make Fun Rides

Magnets

Mapping North America

Mighty Machines

More Places to Visit

My Fish Tank

Our Town

Peanuts

Places to Visit

River Life

Sea and Land Animals

Soil

Spiders Spin Silk

The Car Wash

The Key to Maps

The Rain Forest

The River's Journey

This Is My Street

Tunnels

Turn on a Faucet

Using Rocks

Water Can Change

When a Storm Comes

Where Does the Water Go?

Wind Power

Work Vehicles